{WELCOME}

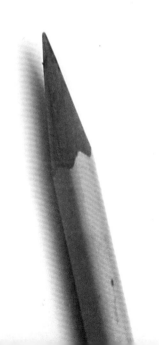

CONTENTS

How to Use This Study

This study has been designed to help you evaluate your understanding of money and the role it plays in your life. Our goal is to explore what God says about the relationship between your faith and your finances. In addition, you will have the opportunity to develop your personal financial map. We've designed this study to work in the context of a small group setting in the following way:

Prior to each session:

Reading – Read the content in this section before the group meeting. This will provide everyone with some context for working through the Discussion Questions.

Practical Application – Complete the Practical Application section before coming to group.

Discussion Starter and Discussion Questions – Answer the questions and be prepared to share with your group.

During each session:

Discussion Starter – A question designed to initiate discussion by focusing on the Practical Application for that week.

Video Segment – A 15–20 minute DVD clip for each week's session provided in the back of this workbook.

Discussion Questions – Questions that should be completed by group members before coming to the meeting and discussed during the group meeting.

Changing Your Mind – A key verse to be memorized during the time between group sessions.

Flip a Coin – Additional material designed to help groups wrestle with real-life financial situations.

You should plan about 90 minutes for a typical group meeting. The following is a sample agenda for your meeting time:

10 minutes: Enjoy snacks and reconnecting.

10 minutes: Talk through the Discussion Starter.

15–20 minutes: Watch the video clip for that session.

35 minutes: Talk through the Discussion Questions and Flip a Coin material.

15–20 minutes: Take time to share prayer requests and pray together.

Feel free to experiment and adapt the schedule to suit your group's unique situation. Most of all, have fun learning and growing together.

INTRODUCTION

Balanced: a condition in which different elements are equal or in the correct proportions.

Success in life usually comes by maintaining balance, or being balanced, with the things that matter most to us.

As children, we need a healthy balance of independence paired with the right amount of parental nurture.

As adults, we're attracted to balanced people. For example, we want to be with people who have a good sense of humor, but who are also comfortable sharing about more serious life issues.

As working individuals, failure to find a balance between our jobs and our families and friends leads to either professional or personal irresponsibility.

All of life requires balance. Without the correct proportions of life's ingredients, we experience instability, resulting in a crash. So what's the secret to maintaining your balance as you navigate through life's circumstances?

Well, if you have ever tried to balance anything, you know that there are three things to remember:

1. **Maintain a reference point.**
   Tightrope walkers know this. Cheerleaders know this. Anybody whose safety depends on maintaining balance will tell you that you need to focus on a reference point.

2. **Make constant corrections.**
   Given an environment with fluctuating circumstances, you have to make constant corrections in order to stay balanced. Try balancing a pole in the palm of your hand and you will soon realize that you have to make constant corrections in order to keep the pole from falling.

3. **Establish a clear objective.**
   What are you trying to do? What are you trying to balance?

We call these the three laws of balance.

However, these laws aren't limited to just balancing physical objects. These laws apply to all areas of life in which you're trying to achieve balance.

For example... your health. If you're trying to eat healthier, lose weight, or observe a balanced diet, you'll need to maintain a reference point, make constant corrections, and have a clear objective.

Trying to find a balance between your professional and personal life? Well, observe these three laws and you'll be off to a good start.

It's the same with your finances. If you weave these three laws into your financial strategy, you'll be balanced. And that's going to be our goal for the next six sessions. We'll discuss what it means to find and maintain a reference point for all your financial decisions. We'll talk about the corrections required to stay balanced. We'll dig deeply to discover what should be driving the decisions we make about our money.

There is, however, one major difference when it comes to balancing a physical object and balancing your finances. Using our example of balancing a pole, if you observe these three laws, you will be able to balance the pole in the palm of your hand. If you ignore one of these laws, the pole will fall. But with financial balance, if you ignore one of the laws... nothing will happen right away! You can violate foundational financial principles and pass through several seasons of your life without realizing that you're in trouble.

That's the tricky thing about trying to achieve financial balance. When there are immediate consequences, we respond right away. If the pole in my palm is about to fall, I'll make immediate adjustments. If my doctor tells me my cholesterol is too high, I'll make immediate adjustments to my diet. But in the realm of personal finances, this principle of immediacy doesn't apply. In fact, financial balance follows a different principle—*the principle of the harvest.*

Sow now. Reap later. Reap greater.

Instead of looking at your immediate situation and asking, *What am I doing wrong?* you have to look at your past decisions. You have to examine your lifestyle. Healthy decisions in the past reap positive results in the future. And to no surprise, unhealthy financial decisions reap negative results. Ask people who abused credit during their college years or their early adult years. Many of them are still struggling with the consequences of those decisions.

What we're not always aware of is that our financial decisions often affect other areas of our lives. Money, or at least our perspectives on money, has that kind of viral influence. Good or bad, money influences our relationship with God, our relationships with our families and friends—the big and small decisions that we make every day. No wonder the Bible has so much to say about money.

Gaining and maintaining financial balance requires that you assess your attitudes and actions about your finances and then make the necessary changes. Otherwise, money can have a grip on you it was never meant to have. That's why we'll discuss not only what God has to say about money, but also concrete principles to move us toward financial balance.

And that is where the rubber meets the road—taking the steps required to achieve financial stability. We'll spend a lot of time discovering new perspectives and attitudes toward money and possessions, but it is critical that you do not stop there. To experience greater intimacy with God and greater freedom in your finances, you must make real changes. To that end, we have provided several Practical Application exercises for each session. Completing these exercises will help you gain clarity on where you are now and where you want to be.

An equally important part of this study is experiencing it with other people. One of the benefits of a healthy small group environment is that it provides accountability. We won't be asking everyone to pass around W2s, but there is an expectation that group members will encourage each other to follow through with the commitments they make.

As we begin this journey together, remember that achieving financial balance will not be easy. The road to financial freedom is filled with challenges, both in how we think about our money and what we do with our money. However, when we not only *hear* what Jesus has to say about financial balance, but also put it into practice, we will have ringside seats to God's faithfulness.

...RTIFICATE

ER THE "TRANSFER OF LAND

...ed in the First Schedule heret...

...ct to the easements and enc...

ER THE "TRANSFER OF LAN

ibed in the First Schedule here

ect to the easements and enc

OPENING THE BOOKS

*Read this before you get together with your group
and answer the Discussion Questions that follow.*

Does the Bible really say that much about money? Isn't it more interested in spiritual things? It might surprise you to find out how often the Bible addresses the issue of money. But when you think about it, it shouldn't be all that surprising, should it? For example, the Bible addresses some of the most important issues about our lives:

> *Relationships*
> *Love*
> *Family*
> *Trust*

These are all issues of the heart. And along those lines, God knows better than anyone else that money … and your attitude toward money … is very much a heart issue.

FAITH AND FINANCES

Finances should be private, shouldn't they? Why bring God into the picture? Why mix faith and finances? After all, what could an invisible God have to do with the very visible stack of unpaid bills on my desk? And what does Jesus have to do with my 401K? How many of us think about God when we swipe our credit cards?

Now we might think about God and say a prayer or two when that credit card is denied or the rent check bounces, but how many of us acknowledge God when our investments are returning double digits? The truth is when it comes to the world of personal finance, many of us tend to think of God as irrelevant—*he's not* … and our faith as separate from our finances—*they aren't*.

Well, guess what? The relationship between faith and finances is not only a Christian thing. All religious systems have something to say about money. In the Bible, God has more things to say about money than about heaven or hell or just about anything else. The Bible suggests that you can't be upside down in your finances and in harmony with God. **In other words, you can't be a committed follower of Jesus Christ and remain irresponsible with your money.**

This study is about more than persuading you to give money to a church or some other religious organization. There is far more in the Bible about *managing* money than about *giving* money. God isn't after your money. Jesus is not in the business of religious fundraising. The Bible doesn't give us exact dollar amounts on how much we should be giving or where exactly we should be giving.

Then what exactly does the Bible say about money?

We will focus on two key verses throughout this study. Here's the first one:

> *For where your treasure is, there your heart will be also.*
> *Matthew 6:21*

This isn't an indictment; it's a natural principle. For example, the principle of gravity tells us that no matter how high we throw a ball up in the air, it will return to the earth. The same is true with your heart and money. Want to know where your heart is? Look at your checkbook.

Now... does God want your checkbook? *No.*

Does God want your heart? *Yes.*

Here's the other verse we will focus on:

> *No one can serve two masters. Either you will hate the one and love the other,*
> *or you will be devoted to the one and despise the other.*
> *You cannot serve both God and money.*
> *Luke 16:13*

Jesus said that the number one competitor for your allegiance to God is money, or material possessions—your stuff. Money is that powerful. It's a conflict you face every day: are you going to serve your stuff or are you going to serve God?

This is why Jesus talked so much about money. He knew that your approach to finances revealed something about your relationship with God. And Jesus wasn't alone in this. The topics of money and possessions are addressed throughout the Bible. And in the following sessions, you'll explore more of what the Bible has to say about being financially balanced.

Again, this study is not about making you feel guilty so you give more to your church or some other organization. Jesus doesn't need your money. He's not trying to get your money. *He wants to make sure that your money doesn't get you.*

Practical Application

What's going on in your financial world? Where are you spending your money? How much are you saving?

The Practical Application for this session is to spy on your money, to keep track of your spending for the week. In fact, this will be an ongoing exercise for the rest of this study. When this study is over, you won't have to wonder where your money goes. You'll know.

If you never open the books, you'll never know the details of your finances. And without the details, your financial picture will always seem a bit cloudy. You would start looking for a new financial advisor if your current one told you, "I'm not exactly sure how your money is allocated…" Why not be sure where your money is going?

We've provided a ledger in the back of this guide that you can use to keep track of your expenses. (An electronic ledger is also available on the DVD under "Additional Resources.") This ledger is not the only tool, or necessarily the best way. If you have a personal finance software tool, feel free to use it. Or if you already have another method of tracking your expenses (maybe the ledger in your checkbook or a spreadsheet), continue to use that. The point is not *how* you track your finances; it is that you *do it.*

So here's what you do: Save all of your receipts from the day and record them in the ledger each night. You can put the receipts in your wallet or in an envelope in your purse. Print out electronic bills or bank statements for items you pay online and record those. If you are married, designate one person to track the spending and go over it together to make sure everything is covered.

Session 1 – Group Discussion

INTRODUCTION

Mystery novels are great entertainment. We eagerly turn the pages to uncover the plot. But the elements that make a great mystery novel, uncertainty and suspense, are not very helpful when it comes to our finances. That's why the first step in this study is to open the books and solve the mystery of where our money goes. In one sense, we want to bring to light our heart's orientation to God and money—*What do we believe?* And in another sense, we need to bring to light our actual spending habits—*Where does our money go?*

The Practical Application for this week will be to track your spending.

DISCUSSION STARTER

If you could change one thing about your current financial situation, what would it be?

....

....

....

....

....

....

....

VIDEO SEGMENT

Watch the Session 1 clip with your group.

DISCUSSION QUESTIONS

1. Do you agree that it is impossible to be a committed follower of Jesus Christ and remain financially irresponsible? Why or why not?

_____

_____

_____

2. What are some of the things that cause people to become financially unbalanced?

_____

_____

_____

3. Read Matthew 6:21. What are some examples in your life of your heart following your stuff?

_____

_____

_____

4. Read Luke 16:13. How does our stuff compete with our devotion to God?

_____

_____

_____

5. When it comes to your finances, what do you think God wants for you (as opposed to what most people think he wants from you)?

....

....

....

....

6. How easy is it for you to trust God with your finances? What would you do differently if you were confident that God wanted the best for you in that area?

....

....

....

....

7. What would you like to see happen in your finances as a result of this study?

....

....

....

....

CHANGING YOUR MIND

For where your treasure is, there your heart will be also.

Matthew 6:21

Flip a Coin

A question about your heart...

Robert always had a shrewd eye for business. As a result, he had profited on nearly all of his business ventures. He had done well for himself (evidenced by his standard of living) and had rarely experienced any financial hardships. Moreover, given his affluence, he was able to be generous... to his church, to local charities, and to international development projects. But during one of his small group meetings, as they studied Jesus' words about two masters: God and money (Luke 16:13), Robert wondered about his allegiance. Was he serving God and seeing his finances through God's perspective? Or was his allegiance to money and his ability to be generous merely a by-product of his financial success?

In the Gospels, Jesus would often speak in absolute terms in order to make a point. For example, while understanding the realities of money and commerce, Jesus made an extreme point about the impossibility of serving both God and money (Luke 16:13). Speaking to the Pharisees, a group well-versed in displays of piety, Jesus knew that you could appear to be making all the right moves with regard to faith and finances. But if your heart were not loyal to God, then you would still be a slave to Money, regardless of your perceived generosity.

Unfortunately, there is no machine you can hook up to your heart to gauge whether you are serving God or Money. Instead, this requires a little bit of soul-searching, honest assessment, and accountability.

Is it possible to have sound financial principles, a generous lifestyle... and still serve Money as a master? Yes. For as Jesus would go on to say in Luke 16:15: *"You are the ones who justify yourselves in the eyes of others, but God knows your heart."* Being financially balanced isn't just about having a balanced checkbook; it's first and foremost about whom our hearts are serving. Is it God? Is it Money? Jesus was right about this: there is no in-between.

Given recent media attention, issues of social justice, charitable giving, and financial management are in vogue. Do you agree that it's possible to be pursuing these practices yet still be serving Money?

Is there a way to determine when you have crossed the line from serving Money to serving God or vice versa? Is there even a line that marks those boundaries?

_____

_____

_____

_____

Prayer Requests

_____

_____

_____

_____

FOR THE NEXT GROUP MEETING:

- Read the content for Session 2.

- Complete the Discussion Questions for Session 2.

- Memorize the "Changing Your Mind" verse for Session 2.

- After reading through Session 2, continue tracking your expenses and complete the Financial Overview.

_____

_____

_____

_____

_____

_____

SESSION 2
READING THE FINE PRINT

*Read this before you get together with your group
and answer the Discussion Questions that follow.*

In the last session, we discussed the need to open up the books and take a sobering look at our finances.

"You've got to be knowing where your money is going."

If you were already in the habit of tracking your expenses, then the application from the previous session should have been easy. But if you rarely track your spending, doing so might have been eye-opening.

This week, let's get to the heart of what shapes our financial decision-making. Let's remind ourselves of what we often forget as we try to balance our ledger sheets.

"What are you trying to accomplish with your money?"

As with most everything else in life, our financial practices are driven by our goals. If our goal is to make a lot of money, we will look for lucrative jobs. If our goal is to live comfortably in retirement, we will set aside money for the future.

What are some of your financial goals?

- Is your goal to provide for your family?
- Is your goal to make as much money as you can?
- Is your goal to save as much money as you can?
- Is your goal to give as much money as you can?
- Is your goal to be financially free?

All of these are honorable goals. Why wouldn't we want to provide for our families? Why wouldn't we want to make money or give money or save money? All of these make sense.

Yet, do they provide a holistic compass for how you should make your financial decisions? Should these goals shape your financial practices? Or should there be something larger ... a bigger idea ... a more comprehensive goal that influences every financial decision you make? What is the **one thing** that should drive our personal finances?

The Bible makes it clear what that **one thing,** that one objective, that one goal, should be.

In the Old Testament, King David was eager to build a temple for God. Up to this point, Israel had been in transit as they fled Egypt and moved from the desert plains into the Promised Land. And while the Israelites had finally settled into their new home and established themselves as formidable people under David's impressive leadership, a temple had never been built for God to reside in. David had hoped to change that by building a temple decorated with grandeur and splendor. But God decided that such a task would be assigned to David's son Solomon.

So, David raised the capital and gathered all the materials and resources so that the temple project would be ready to go under Solomon's leadership. And as David prayed with everyone assembled in anticipation of the temple, we discover his ultimate goal, not only for his finances, but also for his life.

Read 1 Chronicles 29:10-14.

For David, everything in life was about God. He believed everything belonged to God, and everything came from God.

It would have been easy for David to believe otherwise. To those around him, David seemed so accomplished ... so talented ... so productive. David had led Israel through fierce battles and conquered dangerous enemies. Under his leadership, Israel had become a strong nation.

Yet, David knew that everything came from God. All the glory and riches, the accolades and victories, the talents and skills—all of it came from God.

> *But who am I, and who are my people, that we should be able to give as generously as this?*
> *Everything comes from you, and we have given you only what comes from your hand.*
> *1 Chronicles 29:14*

Quite simply, David saw himself as a steward. A steward is a person who has been entrusted with someone else's resources. We often entrust our financial investments to money managers. The principle is the same. The goal of the steward is to grow the owner's assets, not for the personal profit of the money manager, but for the benefit of the owner. When you begin to view yourself as a steward, you will begin to view the money and possessions that God has entrusted you with from a different perspective. You will begin to see them as resources through which you can honor God.

And so, given that everything was from God, David's one goal in life was to honor him.

- What was his objective as a king? To honor God.

- What was his objective as a father? To honor God.

- What was his objective for his finances? To honor God.

And that should be our objective as well. Our objective should be to live with our hands open before God believing that we should honor him with everything we have (since everything we have comes from him in the first place).

You're choosing to live with the mentality, *God's* instead of *mine*. You're choosing to believe all of your talents and gifts and skills ultimately come from God. You're choosing to allow your personal finances to be driven with one thing in mind—honoring God.

And so the question that you and I are faced with is: *How do we do this?*

It can start as a simple prayer as we move forward:

"God, show me how to honor you with everything I have."

Practical Application

COMPLETE THE FINANCIAL OVERVIEW

When someone loans you something, you usually take good care of it. Are you aware of what God has "loaned" you? Do you have a clear picture of your financial situation? The Financial Overview Worksheet in the Appendix has been designed to help you determine exactly what God has entrusted to you. As you work through it, know that you don't have to be accurate down to the penny; rather, estimate the amount of each asset and liability.

Continue to Track Spending

This week you will continue to write down your purchases. Eventually, you will come back to these, put them in categories, and then use them to analyze your monthly spending. Continue to use the ledger in the back of this book, the electronic version on the accompanying DVD, or your own tracking system.

Session 2 – Group Discussion

Introduction

Let's examine a biblical perspective for our finances. The first step is to understand that honoring God should be our goal. The second step is to determine ways we can honor God with our finances. You'll be able to see how you've done so far by completing the Financial Overview and continuing to track your spending in the Practical Application.

Discussion Starter

What did you learn this past week as you tracked your spending? Any surprises? What was helpful about completing the Financial Overview?

....

....

....

....

....

....

Video Segment

Watch the Session 2 clip with your group.

Discussion Questions

1. Up to this point, what has been your goal regarding your money? What has been the main influence on your financial decisions?

_____

_____

_____

_____

2. What does it mean to "honor God" with your life on a day-to-day basis as it relates to your finances?

_____

_____

_____

_____

3. In 1 Chronicles 29, David seems to understand that God was the source of all of the resources available to him. What is the difference between *stewardship* and *ownership*? Why is it hard to see yourself as a steward rather than an owner?

_____

_____

_____

_____

4. How would it change your financial decisions to see yourself as a *steward* of God's gifts and resources?

_____

_____

_____

_____

5. How have people used their money and "stuff" to make an eternal impact on your life?

_____

_____

_____

_____

6. How can you use the money and "stuff" God has given you as tools to make an eternal impact on others?

_____

_____

_____

_____

CHANGING YOUR MIND

Everything comes from you, and we have given you only what comes from your hand.
1 Chronicles 29:14b

FLIP A COIN

A question about tithing...

Sarah and Colin knew they wanted to be generous. They weren't sure what that meant, though. They thought about the church they were attending and different charities that they felt drawn toward. They also considered financially supporting children from foreign countries.

Then they heard a message about tithing and wondered how much they should be giving regularly to the church they were attending. Desiring to honor God with their finances, they still weren't sure how much or what percentage to give to each of these causes. Was giving to the church supposed to be their first priority? Did it matter how they apportioned their giving?

Once you make a decision to honor God with your finances, one common question arises: How much should I regularly give to God? Realizing that God owns everything we have, are we as stewards commanded to give according to the needs we see around us? Or does it honor God to give a consistent percentage on a regular basis?

The Old Testament records "tithing" as a means to honor God with your finances. The Israelites were commanded to bring the best 10 percent of their finances (typically their harvest) to God (Leviticus 27:30). The practice of tithing trained the Israelites to remember who was first in their lives. Realizing that God provided the entire 100 percent, the first 10 percent was to be given to him. In fact, life in the Old Testament was replete with various offerings and charitable giving. There was no denying that all that they had came from God. As a result, giving was ingrained into their relationship with God. When they did not give appropriately, their faith suffered. It wasn't a forced situation. Instead, their faith and their giving (i.e., their finances) were intertwined. The tithe, then, was just a beginning point for their giving, not some budget item that they checked off in order to be right with God.

What does that mean for us today? The compulsory nature of the Old Testament commandment to tithe has been replaced by a greater command to practice generosity (2 Corinthians 9:6-8) at all times. For Jesus and his followers who grew up with the practice of tithing, giving to God meant so much more than just a 10 percent offering. Yet there is no exact amount or percentage that is commanded in the New Testament.

But like any other activity in life, becoming more generous requires a level of discipline. We don't become generous overnight. We need to develop practices in our lives to train us to be more open-handed and charitable with our finances. Tithing, or regular giving (or whatever you'd like to call it), trains us to put God first in regards to our finances.

What arguments have you heard about the command to tithe and give to a local church?

....

....

....

How can a practice of regularly giving help you honor God with your finances?

....

....

....

Prayer Requests

For the Next Group Meeting:

- Read the content for Session 3.
- Complete the Discussion Questions for Session 3.
- Memorize the "Changing Your Mind" verse for Session 3.
- After reading Session 3, work on your Debt Repayment Plan.
- Continue tracking your expenses.

BACK IN THE BLACK

Read this before you get together with your group
and answer the Discussion Questions that follow.

Every time we turn on the television, answer the phone, or surf the Internet, we are bombarded with alluring offers to "spend now and pay later." As a result, more and more people are piling up consumer debt. Today, the credit industry is driven by irresistible offers for unlimited credit. After all, it seems like a good deal. You get to buy stuff *now* with somebody else's money and then pay it off *later*. But there are many reasons you should avoid debt. In this session, we will touch on two of these: *debt makes you a slave; debt limits your freedom.*

Debt makes you a slave.

In the days of the Old Testament, borrowing meant that things were not going well for you. If you were not in a position to obtain something yourself, you would have to borrow from someone else. In Israel's case, if they would remain faithful to God, he would ensure that they would never acquire debt:

> *You will lend to many nations but will borrow from none.*
>
> Deuteronomy 28:12b

Yet, the development of the credit industry has confused this simple concept. Today, if you've generated enough wealth, if you've shown you are responsible with your money, if your credit score if high enough, then you are invited to borrow money from someone else. As a result, by borrowing from someone else, you're exchanging your financial freedom for indebtedness.

The fact that debt makes you a slave might not be intuitive, since debtor's prison and bond-slavery are relics of the past. But throughout most of history, a debtor who couldn't pay up faced either prison or servitude. The consequences of debt are almost as severe today. Debt shackles you. It enslaves you to someone else… someone you have no relationship with… some impersonal financial organization that fails to see you as a person, but just as another number to collect from.

In exchange, to purchase something now, we inherit a future where debt consumes our thoughts, influences our decisions, and inhibits financial stability. The Bible could not be clearer:

The rich rule over the poor, and the borrower is slave to the lender.
Proverbs 22:7

It has been said there are two kinds of people in this world—those who make interest and those who pay interest. When you go into debt, you place yourself with those who pay (and pay dearly). For example, take the cost of running up a balance of $10,000 on a credit card. With a monthly minimum payment of three percent, and an interest rate of 18 percent, it will take you 271 months to be rid of your debt. In that time, you will pay a total of $19,800. What a deal! No wonder the credit card companies encourage you to *just charge it.* Debt costs you more than you think!

Debt limits your freedom.

Our experiences teach us that debt limits our freedom. The Bible teaches the same thing.

Like a city whose walls are broken through is a person who lacks self-control.
Proverbs 25:28

When we don't exercise self-control, guess what? We are no longer in control. We give up our freedom, our ability to be in control. We give up the things that are most valuable to us. Similarly, when we owe people money, they own a part of us. They own a part of our time, our focus, and our energy. This affects our well-being and our relationships with others and with God.

After all, think of the freedom you would experience without debt. How freeing would it be to be able to decide what to do with all that God sends your way? With debt, you have other people dictating how you spend that money. A credit card company forces you to pay a certain amount every month. Next, the car dealership. After that, the mortgage company. What's happened to your financial freedom?

Debt enslaves us and robs us of what could be. It impacts our ability to be generous. How many times have you wanted to express generosity to another person or give to a charity only to feel like you can't because you don't have the financial margin to do so? The Bible advises us to flee from the trap of debt. This is one of those constant corrections that is crucial in order to stay balanced.

Practical Application

The Practical Application for this week requires us to get serious about getting out of debt. It is irresponsible to ignore our debts. Look at the words of Paul recorded in the book of Romans. The Romans had obligations to meet, work to do, and bills and taxes to pay, just like we do. Paul didn't ignore the reality of their situation. He addressed it in a straightforward way.

> *This is also why you pay taxes, for the authorities are God's servants, who give their full time to governing. Give to everyone what you owe: If you owe taxes, pay taxes; if revenue, then revenue; if respect, then respect; if honor, then honor. Let no debt remain outstanding, except the continuing debt to love one another, for whoever loves others has fulfilled the law.*
>
> Romans 13:6–8

As Christians, we are to meet all of our obligations. So how do we do it? There are four steps we can take.

1. **Pray.**
   As your heavenly Father, God is eager to help you get out of debt. Not only does he want to help, he has the resources to do it. Pray that God will give you the wisdom and courage to take the necessary steps to get out of debt. God honors those efforts.

2. **Stop incurring new debt.**
   You can't get out of debt if you keep going into debt. Stop the outflow. For some, this might require that you stop using credit cards and consider an all-cash system. This might seem old-fashioned, and it might be cumbersome, but it's a helpful way to break habits that have unconsciously formed over the years. When it is harder to spend money, you won't spend as much. Whether you use a debit card or cash, the point is to keep from going further into debt. As many of us have experienced, a dependence on credit cards can quickly get you in financial trouble.

3. **Set up an emergency fund.**
   One of the reasons you have debt is because you were not adequately prepared for those unexpected expenses. Your car broke down. You had a major medical expense. Life happened. The last thing you need now is for another financial "emergency" to come along that causes you to spiral further downward. Before you begin to work on a debt repayment plan, protect

yourself by setting up an emergency fund. Financial experts often suggest building an emergency fund to support three months of expenses. Your emergency fund will protect you from incurring debt when the unexpected happens.

4. **Begin working on a debt repayment plan.**
Developing a debt repayment plan is one of the most powerful things you can do. The first step in this process is to face reality—list all of your debts to see just how much you owe. To do this, fill out the Debt Repayment Plan found in the Appendix or on the DVD. Begin by listing your debts from the smallest to the largest amounts (don't worry about the interest rates too much, unless one is a lot higher than the others). Then plan to pay the minimum on all your debts and the maximum you can afford on the smallest debt that you owe. Though it might make more financial sense to begin attacking the debt with the largest interest rate, it is psychologically more rewarding when you begin to eliminate creditors from your list. This gives you the motivation to keep going. With each payoff, roll the amount you were paying into the next smallest debt. Continue with this strategy until you are debt free!

In our example, Bob has set aside $600 for debt repayment.

Item	Total Owed	Minimum Payment	New Payment
Home Improvement Store	$ 150	$ 15	$110
Department Store	$ 250	$ 10	$ 10
Credit Card #1	$ 500	$ 75	$ 75
Credit Card #2	$1,500	$ 90	$ 90
Car Loan	$4,000	$250	$250
Student Loan	$4,000	$ 65	$ 65

After paying off the first credit card, his new debt repayment plan would look like this:

Item	Total Owed	Minimum Payment	New Payment
Department Store	$ 250	$ 10	$120
Credit Card #1	$ 500	$ 75	$ 75
Credit Card #2	$1,500	$ 90	$ 90
Car Loan	$4,000	$250	$250
Student Loan	$4,000	$ 65	$ 65

Now it's your turn.

CONTINUE TO TRACK YOUR SPENDING

You will continue to write down your purchases for the week. Later, you will come back to these, put them in categories, and then use them to analyze your monthly budget.

Session 3 – Group Discussion

INTRODUCTION

Getting into debt is easy. Getting out of debt is another story. Our appetites, our desire for bigger and better, and our accessibility to borrow money, all make it easy to overlook the fact that debt enslaves us. The idea of "have now, pay later" can shackle us and throw our financial worlds out of balance.

Discussion Starter

After working through the Practical Application for this week, what is your strategy for getting out of or staying out of debt?

_____

_____

_____

_____

_____

_____

_____

Video Segment

Watch the Session 3 clip with your group.

Discussion Questions

1. Describe your family of origin's approach to finances. Were things tight? How did they use debt? Was it a source of tension for your family?

_____

_____

_____

_____

2. What has been your experience with debt?

_____

_____

_____

3. In what ways does debt limit freedom? Can you give any personal examples?

_____

_____

_____

4. What makes it so difficult to get out of debt?

_____

_____

_____

5. What are the benefits of living debt-free?

_____

_____

_____

6. Is going into debt always unwise? When is it wise?

_____

_____

_____

CHANGING YOUR MIND

The rich rule over the poor,
and the borrower is slave to the lender.
Proverbs 22:7

FLIP A COIN

A question about debt...

Using images like slavery and imprisonment, we have suggested that debt is a dark financial spiral to be avoided at all costs. The Proverbs speak alarmingly against accumulating debt. Other passages from the Bible suggest that having to borrow from another person is a curse, whereas being in a position to lend is a blessing. Yet in today's economy, are there times when borrowing would be appropriate?

The ability to pay cash for all your purchases frees you from the financial pressures of debt. However, not everyone has the luxury of being able to pay cash for some of life's larger items. In fact, some financial counselors argue that certain types of debt can be included in a different category. These would include such things as home mortgages or educational expenses. The idea being that these exceptions have built-in systems of collateral that can be sold if the debtor can't pay, or they have an appreciating level of value.

Regardless of how you categorize debt, there is one thing that the Bible is certain about: God discourages it. Not only should we do what we can to avoid it, in those cases where we do incur debt, we should make every effort to get out of debt as soon as possible.

Both Tom and Cheryl came from families that had taught them sound financial principles. Having had the good fortune of their parents to pay for their educations, these newlywed college graduates had steady jobs with no outstanding debt. Five years into their marriage, with a one-year-old toddler, Tom and Cheryl made a decision to start looking for their first home. Yet even with their savings, they knew they would have to apply for a home loan, and, as a result, experience debt for the first time. On top of that, Tom's car was on its last leg and would soon need to be replaced, further depleting their savings.

Cheryl's family had always abided by a no-debt financial plan. As a result, she suggested that they use their savings to purchase a used car with cash and wait several more years to purchase their first home. She believed that incurring any kind of debt reflected an inability to depend on God for your needs.

On the other hand, Tom's family benefitted from pursuing various financial opportunities, often taking on manageable levels of debt in exchange for financial gain later on. As a result, Tom wanted to explore options that allowed them to purchase a car as well as to take advantage of the current economic conditions that made home ownership much more affordable.

Are there life circumstances that necessitate going into debt?

What are some examples of "wise" and "foolish" debt?

What safeguards have you created to ensure that the debt you are incurring is indeed "wise" debt?

Prayer Requests

FOR THE NEXT GROUP MEETING

- Read the content for Session 4.

- Complete the Discussion Questions for Session 4.

- Memorize the "Changing Your Mind" verse for Session 4.

- After reading Session 4, work on your Giving Plan.

- Continue tracking your expenses.

SESSION 4
CREATING A NEW LINE ITEM

Read this before you get together with your group and answer the Discussion Questions that follow.

Standard household budgets include line items for...

...living expenses.

...food.

...insurance.

...entertainment.

...savings.

...emergencies.

But do we have a line item for... *giving?*

While few households think they are downright selfish, giving tends to be an afterthought. If you have some extra at the end of the month, then you can exercise some generosity and give some of your money away. *"Sure, I've got a couple extra bucks to support some charitable cause or to give to my church."*

But more times than not, most of us don't feel we have enough at the end of the month. This is because our lifestyles tend to chase our incomes. Now, there are certainly those who have a lot of extra cash at the end of the month. But the truth is, most of us have some "extra." We have more square footage, more cars, more clothes, more food, and more discretionary income than most of the world. This becomes increasingly evident whenever we're around people who have a lot less than we do.

The problem is not the extra. The problem is our *view* of the extra. Until we understand why we have so much, we'll never know what to do with it. Jesus told a story about a man who answered the *why* question all wrong. He told us the story so we could get it right.

41

The rich man in this parable was confused. First, he took credit for the abundance that "the ground" yielded. In an agricultural society, it should have been obvious that the abundance of his harvest had less to do with him and more to do with external factors. Farmers are always at the mercy of influences over which they have no control. But the rich man didn't see it that way. He believed he was solely responsible for the abundance and could do whatever he wanted with it. It never crossed his mind that the extra he had been blessed with was not for his consumption. So he came up with a plan for storing his extra to secure his own future. And if the story had ended there, we would probably consider him a role model for saving up for the future. But the story doesn't end there. Though he planned ahead, he didn't plan far enough ahead.

When we meet people like this, we are usually envious of their fortunes. But God sees it differently. Instead of calling him wise, or putting him on the list of the world's wealthiest people, God called him a fool (verse 20). The rich man assumed that all his money guaranteed him the time to consume it. But he ran out of time before he ran out of money. And the question that God posed to the man was this: *Then who will get what you have prepared for yourself?* And the obvious answer was—*somebody else.* You see, in the end, all of his possessions were distributed to others, but not because he was generous.

It is important to note that God did not call him a fool for being rich. God called him a fool because he didn't know *why* he was rich. He wasn't criticized for *having* extra, but for thinking the extra was for him. And notice the last verse . . . the moral of the story.

> *This is how it will be with those who store up things for*
> *themselves but are not rich toward God.*
> *Luke 12:21*

Jesus sets up the contrast between storing up selfishly and being rich toward God. For what you choose to do with your extra is an indication of who or what controls your heart. Are you living your life in the abundance of your possessions or are you being rich toward God?

Now what does it mean to be rich toward God? It is defined a few verses later:

> *Sell your possessions and give to the poor. Provide purses for yourselves that will*
> *not wear out, a treasure in heaven that will never fail, where no thief comes near*
> *and no moth destroys. For where your treasure is, there your heart will be also.*
> *Luke 12:33–34*

Does this mean that Jesus wants us to sell everything we have and give it all away? For some people trapped under the slavery of consumption, that might be the simplest way of escaping their bondage. For most others, it might require being more intentional about giving. Through these passages, Jesus wants us to realize the importance of a generous heart. According to Jesus, the reason we've been given abundance is not to secure our futures…at least not in this life. The reason for our abundance is so we can provide for the needs of others. In that way, we become wealthy in a different sense.

The landowner suffered a total reversal at death. He lost everything in this life and had nothing to show for it in the next life. He didn't just lose his life; he lost everything he considered valuable. In the words of Jesus, he was a fool; a fool that most of us would have envied had we known him; a fool that many of us have a tendency to emulate. But he was financially unbalanced and didn't even know it—until it was too late to do anything about it.

Practical Application

GIVING PLAN

This week, you'll work on the Giving Plan. You'll assess your current giving and develop a long-term plan for investing the money God has given you to help others. The Giving Plan can be found in the Appendix or on the DVD.

We spend countless hours determining what we should invest in and what purchases we should make. We should be as attentive when it comes to allocating the money we have set aside to give away.

CONTINUE TO TRACK SPENDING

You will continue to write down your purchases for the week. Eventually, you will come back to these, put them in categories, and use them to develop your monthly budget.

Session 4 – Group Discussion

INTRODUCTION

So far we've looked at where money comes from. To do that, we've had to answer the "who" question: Who does our money come from? The question we need to ask now is a little more uncomfortable. It's the "why" question: *Why* do we have so much?

DISCUSSION STARTER

What did you find helpful as you worked through the Giving Plan? Were you surprised at how much or how little you currently spend on helping others?

VIDEO SEGMENT

Watch the Session 4 clip with your group.

DISCUSSION QUESTIONS

1. Do you consider yourself to be rich? Why or why not?

2. Why is it so difficult to recognize greed in the mirror? What are some of the signs?

_____

_____

_____

3. What prevents us from sharing what we have with others?

_____

_____

_____

4. When have you been able to meet someone else's needs? How did that feel?

_____

_____

_____

5. Why is it important to be a consistent and percentage giver?

_____

_____

_____

6. What steps can you take to consistently practice generosity with your finances?

_____

_____

_____

Then he said to them,
"Watch out!
Be on your guard against all kinds of greed;
life does not consist in an abundance of possessions."
Luke 12:15

FLIP A COIN

A question about giving...

After listening to a compelling talk on giving during the recent financial series at church, Melissa and Thomas wanted to support the missions department at their local church, particularly as the department was planning to send a number of short-term teams to Africa. The following week, as they decided how much they would give, they also heard a talk on the perils of debt. Wrestling with their desire to honor God with their finances, Melissa and Thomas were unsure as to whether to give or to pay off their existing credit card debt first.

What guidelines should they use to make their decision?

_____

_____

_____

Should they maintain a certain percentage toward giving or make adjustments to decrease their level of debt?

_____

_____

_____

There is no doubt that God wants us to be generous with our finances, generous with our personal stuff, our extra stuff, our money, our time. In response to a surplus in our lives, we should be generous, not asking God *if*, but *how* we can express his generosity in our lives to others.

But we also know that God isn't a big fan of debt. To be in debt is a debilitating condition where we become enslaved to someone else instead of experiencing freedom with our finances. God advises us to avoid debt, and if we are in debt, to pay our debtors as soon as possible.

And so is there an order of priority? Do we give or pay off debt first?

Some Christians suggest that it would be a poor example not to pay off their debts. And so their priority is to pay off their bills. They might completely stop giving anything to God in order to move themselves out of debt. Or they might reduce their giving in order to make their minimum (or larger) monthly payments. God understands, right?

But consider the various passages in Scripture that point to God's provision when his people decide to honor him first (Malachi 3:10; Luke 6:38). It seems like generosity has to be a staple in our lives, regardless of our financial condition. It doesn't seem right to ask God to help us get balanced, yet not be faithful in our giving.

Is there a way to both give and pay off our debts?

....

....

....

Can we cut our spending in other areas?

....

....

....

Can we take steps toward reducing debt without sacrificing generosity?

Prayer Requests

For the Next Group Meeting

- Read the content for Session 5.

- Complete the Discussion Questions for Session 5.

- Memorize the "Changing Your Mind" verse for Session 5.

- After reading Session 5, work on your Actual Monthly Spending Worksheet.

- Continue tracking your expenses.

MANAGING YOUR EXPENSES

Read this before you get together with your group
and answer the Discussion Questions that follow.

We live in one of the most affluent cultures the world has ever known. For example, most of us own one car, if not more. Our homes often have an extra room for guests that remains vacant a vast majority of the time. As a result, we should be some of the most content, satisfied people on the face of the earth. Yet, while we might not readily admit it, most of us want more stuff. To make matters more difficult, everywhere we go we are enticed by advertisements and images of the newest, must-have things. In other words, we grow hungry... for more.

Unfortunately, an appetite is never completely satisfied. No matter how much you eat in one setting, you will get hungry again. And so it is with much of our material possessions:

"This is the computer of all computers!"

"This is all the house we'll ever need."

"If I can just land one big account, I'll be set."

What inevitably happens is that in a few years, you'll be looking to upgrade... upgrade your computer... upgrade your car... upgrade your home. No matter how much you eat, no matter how much you have, that appetite will never be satisfied. In fact, the more you feed an appetite, the bigger it gets.

But what fuels our appetites to want more? What makes us hunger for bigger, newer, faster, shinier? One word: *discontentment.*

Discontentment: the dissatisfaction I have with what I have.

We realize our discontentment when we become aware that there is something bigger and better. If we never saw a bigger home or a shinier car, then we wouldn't be so discontent with our current one. But when we become aware that there is a whole new world of "new, improved, bigger, shinier," then we become dissatisfied and we develop an appetite for more. And in order to obtain those things, we often sacrifice our financial freedom. We become unbalanced.

So how can we quiet the rumblings of our discontentment? Paul's words to Timothy —a young church leader—contain an answer and a warning.

> *But godliness with contentment is great gain. For we brought nothing into the world, and we can take nothing out of it. But if we have food and clothing, we will be content with that. Those who want to get rich fall into temptation and a trap and into many foolish and harmful desires that plunge people into ruin and destruction. For the love of money is a root of all kinds of evil. Some people, eager for money, have wandered from the faith and pierced themselves with many griefs.*
>
> *But you, man of God, flee from all this, and pursue righteousness, godliness, faith, love, endurance and gentleness.*
>
> 1 Timothy 6:6-11

In other words, Paul gives us a strategy to fight discontentment. Basically, Paul says that the idea of "great gain" is not about acquiring more stuff in this life because when we die, we can't take anything with us. Instead, "great gain" is about incorporating our devotion to God with an inner satisfaction with what we have.

Paul continues with a warning to the wealthy in verse 9: *you are headed down a slippery slope.* You will find that when you feed your discontentment, you not only need to acquire more and more stuff, but one day you might find that it has taken you to a place you never meant to go. Take, for example, the wealthy corporate executive who winds up breaking the law in his quest for more. The love of money is the root of all kinds of evil. The more we have, the more we want. Can you think of some dumb things you have done in your life in order to feed your discontentment?

Ruined relationships?

Moral failures?

So, is there another way? Perhaps there's a solution to your discontentment.

Paul suggests that we pursue good things . . . things that are worthy of our energy and focus. He identifies a way we can leverage our dissatisfaction for our benefit:

Command those who are rich in this present world not to be arrogant nor to put their hope in wealth, which is so uncertain, but to put their hope in God, who richly provides us with everything for our enjoyment. Command them to do good, to be rich in good deeds, and to be generous and willing to share.

1 Timothy 6:17–18

In other words, be discontent about something else! Instead of being in an environment where you're constantly aware of what you don't have, place yourself in an environment where you become aware of how much you really do have. Put simply, stop pursuing how to "get rich" and start pursuing how to "be rich."

One practical way of redirecting your dissatisfaction is by becoming aware of what other people need. As a result, you'll become less driven by what you don't have. When it comes to your finances, don't obsess about how much you can accumulate for yourself, focus on how you can leverage your wealth for the good of others. That's the power of awareness. When you become aware of others' needs, you become discontent toward injustice. Your attention turns to others, not just what you want. And ironically, this actually leads to treasure:

In this way they will lay up treasure for themselves as a firm foundation for the coming age, so that they may take hold of the life that is truly life.

1 Timothy 6:19

Practical Application

ACTUAL MONTHLY SPENDING

This week, you will enter your transactions from the first four weeks of this study into the Actual Monthly Spending Worksheet in the Appendix (or in the electronic version found on the DVD). This will enable you to analyze your spending for the month. It will help you match up your actual spending to your budget categories and compare them. Next to each major category (housing, transportation, insurance, etc.) total the subcategories underneath it.

Completing this exercise will provide you with a snapshot of where your money has gone. This will give you the opportunity to step back and analyze your spending decisions. Is this where you wanted your money to go?

Session 5 – Group Discussion

INTRODUCTION

Discontentment is robbing our generation. We are bombarded daily with messages that tell us to be dissatisfied with our current circumstances. We walk around with the gnawing sense that we need to upgrade everything. The truth is that more money doesn't quench this hunger; it only causes it to increase. So, what are we to do? In this session, we will discuss how we can leverage our discontentment for good.

DISCUSSION STARTER

When were you the most content in your life? When did you feel the least pressured to accumulate wealth and/or acquire more stuff?

_____

_____

_____

_____

_____

_____

VIDEO SEGMENT

Watch the Session 5 clip with your group.

DISCUSSION QUESTIONS

1. "Discontentment is robbing our generation." Do you agree with this statement? If so, why?

_____

_____

_____

_____

2. Has an increase in your income satisfied your appetite? How does your income level affect your level of contentment?

_____

_____

_____

_____

3. What is the danger that comes with "being rich"? How have you seen this in your life and the lives of others?

_____

_____

_____

_____

4. Where do you need to draw the line and be content with what you have?

_____

_____

_____

_____

5. What are the benefits of being rich in good deeds and generous to others?

_____

_____

_____

6. What could you do this week to fight discontentment by becoming more aware of what someone else doesn't have?

....

....

....

....

Changing Your Mind

Command those who are rich in this present world
not to be arrogant nor to put their hope in wealth,
which is so uncertain,
but to put their hope in God,
who richly provides us with everything for our enjoyment.
1 Timothy 6:17

Flip a Coin

A question about spending...

Midway through their study in Balanced, several of the members in Janet's small group wanted the group to sponsor a child from a third world country. One of the members in the group, however, said she couldn't contribute because of her current financial situation. This raised a level of tension with some of the other group members since this was the same member that regularly showed up to her small group wearing new designer clothes. They wondered if she really couldn't afford to contribute or if it was more of a "I could, but choose not to" attitude.

What does it mean to honor God with your financial lifestyle?

....

....

....

Are Christians called to live within their means or to live more simply?

....

....

....

Does living more simply equate to having less stuff or more inexpensive stuff?

....

....

....

On the one hand, Christ commanded his followers, *"Do not store up for yourselves treasures on earth"* (Matthew 6:19). Christ challenged his followers saying, *"… those of you who do not give up everything you have cannot be my disciples"* (Luke 14:33). In one famous example, he went so far as to tell a rich young man to *"Go, sell everything you have and give to the poor, and you will have treasure in heaven"* (Mark 10:21).

On the other hand, God does not extend a universal command to take a vow of poverty. The Bible includes wealthy landowners as well as those of low economic standing amongst God's followers. In fact, we can probably agree that it's not how much money we have but what we do with that money that God is more concerned with. This inevitably raises a very difficult question: *How much is too much?*

For example, although we might be able to afford a $100,000 car, should we be content with a $20,000 car? $40,000? $60,000? How much is too much? How do we manage the tension of enjoying some luxuries in life against the trappings of materialism?

This kind of discussion is bound to touch on a number of sensibilities. The answer to the question "How much is too much?" is going to be subjective. Is it possible that God might challenge some people to sell all their possessions and venture out into the unknown? Sure, but more often than not, it's a matter of asking God to guide us as we seek wisdom in our day-to-day financial decisions. Two questions can help along the way…

1. Do your current spending habits increase or decrease your capacity to live generously?

2. In order to balance out the models of extravagance found in our culture, how can we surround ourselves with models of simple living or lavish giving?

Prayer Requests

For the Next Group Meeting:

- Read the content for Session 6.

- Complete the Discussion Questions for Session 6.

- Memorize the "Changing Your Mind" verse for Session 6.

- After reading Session 6, work on your Spending Plan.

- Continue tracking your expenses.

SESSION 6
DEVELOPING A PLAN

Read this before you get together with your group and answer the Discussion Questions that follow.

"Help me, God!"

How often have you said those words? Our prayers take on a completely new dimension when we're experiencing hardships or difficulties. And there's nothing wrong with that; God invites us to call out to him and ask him for help. But if we're only involving him when things are bad, we turn God into an afterthought, something like a spiritual vending machine of hope. He becomes a last resort, a last priority, receiving only the leftovers of our attention once we've exhausted every other option.

In this final session, let's fix that. In developing a simple plan for our personal finances, we are actually establishing an alternative way of thinking... not just about our money, but about where God fits into our lives.

When we consider where our money goes, we have five options:

1. Spend.

2. Repay debt.

3. Pay taxes.

4. Save.

5. Give.

This tends to be our order of priority as well. The first four are about "me." (Paying taxes isn't much of an option.) The last priority is about God and others. In other words, God gets the leftovers. What does God have to say about that?

Read Malachi 3:7-10.

Let's set this passage into its proper context. From Israel's early days, they had made a covenant with God to bring him their tithes and offerings. They would bring their firstfruits—the best crops and livestock—and offer those to God as a reflection of their priorities. Yet, over the years, Israel began to offer God the leftovers, the worst of their crops, and the lamest of their animals.

So, in response, God says, "Hey, get back to trusting me; get back to making me your foremost priority":

> *Return to me, and I will return to you… see if I will not throw*
> *open the floodgates of heaven and pour out so much blessing*
> *that there will not be room enough to store it.*
> *Malachi 3:7b, 10b*

The principle behind that promise to the Israelites still echoes loudly today. And it's not just a financial issue; it's a heart issue—an issue of priorities. Throw open the doors and invite God into your life. See what happens!

Jesus makes it very clear:

> *But seek first his kingdom and his righteousness, and all*
> *these things will be given to you as well.*
> *Matthew 6:33*

God doesn't promise greater riches or infinite wealth. But he does promise that if you trust him, he will take care of you. And when you're in the midst of financial turmoil, believing that can bring an invaluable sense of comfort and peace.

REORDERING YOUR PRIORITIES

The challenge presented in this last session is to develop a wise solution, a life-long plan for your finances that will ensure you move to a place of peace, contentment, and purpose. In doing so, you will become balanced.

So, what's a wise plan?

Give first, save second, and live off the rest.

This incorporates all the principles we have been discussing throughout this study. How does this work? It's simple. When you are paid, the first check you write is for giving; the second check you write is for savings; and then you live off the rest.

When the first check you write is for giving, you are saying with your actions, "God first." When you make the decision that giving a percentage of your income is your top priority, you are, in essence, inviting him into your finances. Moreover, making giving your first priority serves as a healthy reminder that you are a steward of the resources God has entrusted to you. This decision to practice generosity toward God and others with open hands instead of closed fists will break the power of greed and bridle your discontentment.

When the second check you write is for your future, you are making the sacrifice now so that you will have provision for later. You are choosing not to consume everything you have and choosing to store away for the future. Cars break down, roofs leak, and jobs are lost. It is wise to make preparations for the uncertainty of tomorrow. When the time comes to replace your car, send the kids to college, or retire, you will be prepared. When you pay yourself second, you prepare yourself for the known and unknown expenses that are coming your way.

After the first two checks, you are free to live wisely off the rest. Completing the Practical Application for this session will help you develop this principle of "give, save, live." Feel free to tweak the Spending Plan that you'll create so that you get the most out of the money God has entrusted you with. Over time, you will have the margin to make those first two checks even larger as you weed out the waste and put more money toward the things that will last.

One final note on this step. The "give, save, live" principle is easy to pass on to your kids, even when they're young. Perhaps your parents set you on a track for financial wisdom, but for many of us, this wasn't the case. It doesn't have to be that way for your children. You can begin to pass on wise money principles. One way is to collect three glass jars and label one *Giving*, one *Savings*, and one *Spending*. Every time they get money, have them put 10 percent in the Giving jar, 10 percent in the Savings jar, and the other 80 percent in the Spending jar. If you teach them from the beginning to put their finances in order, you will set them up for a lifetime of financial stability.

Practical Application

SPENDING PLAN

Now that you've tracked where you've been spending your money, it's time to start telling it where it *should* go. That is the goal of a spending plan (a budget!). A spending plan allows you to decide in advance where your money will go, instead of wondering where it went. That way you won't "run out of money before you run out of month."

While these past several weeks have been a snapshot of your spending, they probably don't reflect some expenses that occur periodically. For example, if you pay your auto insurance twice a year, divide the yearly total by twelve and insert that amount into your Actual Monthly Spending Plan. Try to make sure that your spending plan reflects all the expenses you expect to have in the coming year.

Every dollar of your available income should be placed in one of the spending plan categories. After your first pass, subtract your category totals (#2–#13) from your income (#1). If the amount is negative (more expenses than income), plan to make some cutbacks in your spending. We have arranged the spending plan categories from needs to wants. When you look for areas in which to make cutbacks, start at the bottom and work your way up.

If the amount is positive (you haven't yet allocated all of your income), direct your margin to paying off additional debt, giving, or savings.

Session 6 – Group Discussion

INTRODUCTION

This is the final session in our study. Thus far, we have made the case that you can't be financially irresponsible and follow Jesus wholeheartedly. This is because how you handle money is a spiritual issue. And we're not simply referring to your giving, but how you manage all of your money and possessions. After all, there is nothing more telling about what you value than your receipts and the items in your checkbook.

DISCUSSION STARTER

How will working with a spending plan help you align the way you spend your money with your personal priorities?

_____

_____

_____

_____

VIDEO SEGMENT

Watch the Session 6 clip with your group.

DISCUSSION QUESTIONS

1. Why does it make sense to choose to live off a percentage of your income?

_____

_____

_____

2. What challenges might prevent you from setting apart a portion of your income and practicing "give, save, live"?

_____

_____

_____

3. Does it matter what percentages you choose to give, save, and live on? Have you heard any helpful suggestions from financial experts? Does the Bible offer any suggestions?

----

4. What are some good benchmark percentages for you to consider?

----

5. Prior to this study, how intentional were you (if at all) about allocating a certain percentage of your income to giving, saving, and living?

----

6. Going forward, what is your plan for staying out of debt?

----

7. How will you manage the money and possessions that God has given you differently because of this study?

_____

_____

_____

CHANGING YOUR MIND

But seek first his kingdom and his righteousness,
and all these things will be given to you as well.
Matthew 6:33

FLIP A COIN

A question about saving...

"Make as much as you can, save as much as you can, and give as much as you can."
John Wesley

Billy had always subscribed to the "give, save, live" philosophy. He always gave a certain amount from his paycheck to his local church. He would save a certain percentage and then live off the rest. As his salary increased, he continued to give the same amount, live off the same amount, but increased the amount that he would save. By increasing his savings, he felt he would achieve "financial independence." Although he had no immediate plans for the future, he continued to save as much as he could.

Is there a difference between saving for the future and hoarding a stockpile of wealth?

During a gasoline shortage, one man stored large supplies of gasoline in his garage saying, "I have to get as much as I can before the hoarders get it!"

There's no question as to the merits of saving in the Bible. The Proverbs are filled with illustrations regarding the wisdom of saving for the future, setting money aside now to prepare for events later on. But is it possible to save in such a way that you achieve a level of financial independence where you no longer need God because you have created your own financial safety net?

Alongside God's encouragement to save are his cautions against hoarding. During Israel's march through the desert, God cautioned them from hoarding the daily food he would provide for them by taking only what they needed for the day (Exodus 16). In the New Testament, Jesus told a parable of a certain rich man who saved for the future without regard for using those monies to be rich toward God (Luke 12).

So on one extreme you have those who choose not to save at all (and are either giving away or spending away all their extra). And on the other end of the spectrum, you have those who hoard all their savings for a future rainy day that will never come.

Managing this tension is a difficult one for we do not want to presume on God nor do we want to replace our dependence on him. As God blesses us, we want to be a channel of that blessing, today and in the future, rather than a stockpiling storehouse.

So, what do we need to do in order to save, yet keep open hands toward giving and trusting God for our future?

_____

_____

_____

_____

How can we balance saving for the future with maintaining our dependence on God?

_____

_____

_____

_____

EPILOGUE

Remember the three laws of balance?

We started with those . . . and we'll end with those.

1. **Maintain a reference point.**

2. **Make constant corrections.**

3. **Have a clear objective.**

Of all the things you've learned over the past six sessions, if you keep these three laws in check, you'll be well on your way toward financial balance.

As is the case with most small group studies, completing the final chapter does not mean you've reached the end of the road. We hope that you've made some serious inroads into gaining financial balance. But this study is subtitled *Gaining and Maintaining Financial Stability* because once you gain a level of balance, there is a lifelong process of maintaining that balance . . . a consistent discipline of incorporating your faith with your finances. Beyond just having a balanced checkbook, our goal has always been to maintain a balanced perspective on finances mixed in with a healthy dose of practical exercises in order to stay on track.

It should be clear that God has never been in the business of pursuing your money. Rather, he's much more concerned with pursuing you and your heart, wanting you to experience freedom from a life of financial slavery, freedom from the trappings of greed. Because he knows that no matter how full our wallets, purses, or savings accounts might be, we'll never know genuine freedom until we experience financial balance.

{ APPENDIX }

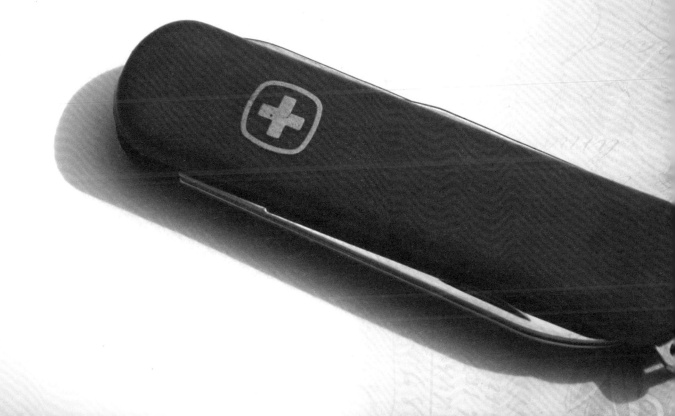

Track Your Spending

DATE	DESCRIPTION	AMOUNT

An electronic version of this document is available on the DVD.

Financial Overview

ASSETS

Checking Account ....

Savings ....

Investments (Stocks, bonds, etc.) ....

Cash Value of Life Insurance ....

Real Estate (Home and any rentals) ....

Business Value ....

Vehicles ....

Personal Property (Furniture, jewelry, etc.) ....

Retirement (401k, IRA, pension, etc.) ....

Other ....

LIABILITIES

Credit Card Debt ....

Automobile Loans ....

Mortgages ....

Business Loans ....

Education Loans ....

Past Due Bills ....

Other Liabilities ....

NET WORTH

(Assets – Liabilities)

An electronic version of this document is available on the DVD.

Debt Repayment Schedule

Item	Total Owed	Minimum Payment	New Payment

An electronic version of this document is available on the DVD.

Giving Plan

WHERE SHOULD YOU GIVE?

The Bible does not spell out in detail where we should give, but we can discern certain guidelines for our giving.

1. We should give to the local church. The local church is God's unique institution in the world. It is our opportunity to provide for those leading the church (1 Timothy 5:17-18) and to support its missionaries (Philippians 4:15-19).

2. We should also give to the poor. God has a special concern for those in need (Matthew 25:34-40), as well as widows and orphans (James 1:27). Beyond these priorities, there are also many organizations and individuals worthy of support.

CURRENT GIVING	ORGANIZATION	AMOUNT
Local Church		
Other		
Other		
Total		
% of Income		

FUTURE GIVING PLAN

In light of your current assessment, what percentage of your income would you like to move toward giving?

% of Income		
Total		
Local Church		
Other		
Other		

What must happen for you to get from where you are to where you want to be?

An electronic version of this document is available on the DVD.

Actual Monthly Spending

INCOME

Income #1	
Income #2	
Alimony/Child Support	
Other	

GIVING

Church	
Missions	
Other	

SAVINGS

Emergency	
Retirement (401k)	
Retirement (IRA)	
College	
Investments	

INCOME TAXES

Federal	
State	
Social Security	
Medicare	

An electronic version of this document is available on the DVD.

Debt

IRS	
Credit Card #1	
Credit Card #2	
Credit Card #3	
Credit Card #4	
Credit Card #5	
Student Loans	
Other	
Other	
Other	

Housing

Mortgage/Rent	
Home Insurance	
Property Taxes	
City Taxes	
Association Dues	
Telephone	
Electricity & Gas	
Water, Sewage, Trash	
Cable/TV/Internet	
Maintenance	
Other	
Other	

Transportation

Car Payment #1	
Car Payment #2	
Auto Insurance	
Registration/License	
Gas	
Tolls & Parking	
Oil & Maintenance	
Other	

Insurance

Health	
Life	
Dental & Vision	
Disability	
Long-term Care	
Umbrella	
Other	

Food & Household

Food	
Other	
Other	
Other	

HEALTH

Medical Expenses ....

Fitness ....

Counselor ....

Other ....

Other ....

PERSONAL

Alimony/Child Support ....

Childcare ....

Education ....

Beauty & Barber ....

Cell Phone ....

Clothes ....

Household Décor ....

Gifts ....

Cleaning ....

Financial Services ....

Security System ....

Pest Control ....

Landscaping ....

Pets ....

Other ....

Other ....

Entertainment

Vacation	
Eating Out	
Events	
Music	
Other	
Other	

Total Spending

Margin *(Income–Spending)*

Spending Plan

Income

Income #1	
Income #2	
Alimony/Child Support	
Other	
Total	

Giving

	Target %:	Actual %:
Church		
Other		
Other		
Total		

Savings

	Target %:	Actual %:
Emergency		
Retirement (401k)		
Retirement (IRA)		
College		
Investments		
Total		

Income Taxes

	Target %:	Actual %:
Federal		
State		
Social Security		
Medicare		
Total		

An electronic version of this document is available on the DVD.

Debt

	Target %:	Actual %:
IRS		
Credit Card #1		
Credit Card #2		
Credit Card #3		
Credit Card #4		
Credit Card #5		
Student Loans		
Other		
Other		
Other		
Total		

Housing

	Target %	Actual %:
Mortgage/Rent		
Home Insurance		
Property Taxes		
City Taxes		
Association Dues		
Telephone		
Electricity & Gas		
Water, Sewage, Trash		
Cable/TV/Internet		
Maintenance		
Other		
Other		
Total		

Transportation   Target %:   Actual %:

Car Payment #1

Car Payment #2

Auto Insurance

Registration/License

Gas

Tolls & Parking

Oil & Maintenance

Other

Total

Insurance   Target %:   Actual %:

Health

Life

Dental & Vision

Disability

Long Term Care

Umbrella

Other

Total

Food & Household   Target %:   Actual %:

Food

Other

Other

Other

Total

HEALTH

	Target %:	Actual %:
Medical Expenses		
Fitness		
Counselor		
Other		
Other		
TOTAL		

PERSONAL

	Target %:	Actual %:
Alimony/Child Support		
Childcare		
Education		
Beauty & Barber		
Cell Phone		
Clothes		
Household Décor		
Gifts		
Cleaning		
Financial Services		
Security System		
Pest Control		
Landscaping		
Pets		
Other		
Other		
TOTAL		

Entertainment

Target %:   Actual %:

Vacation	
Eating Out	
Events	
Music	
Other	
Other	
Total	

Total Spending

Margin *(Income–Spending)*

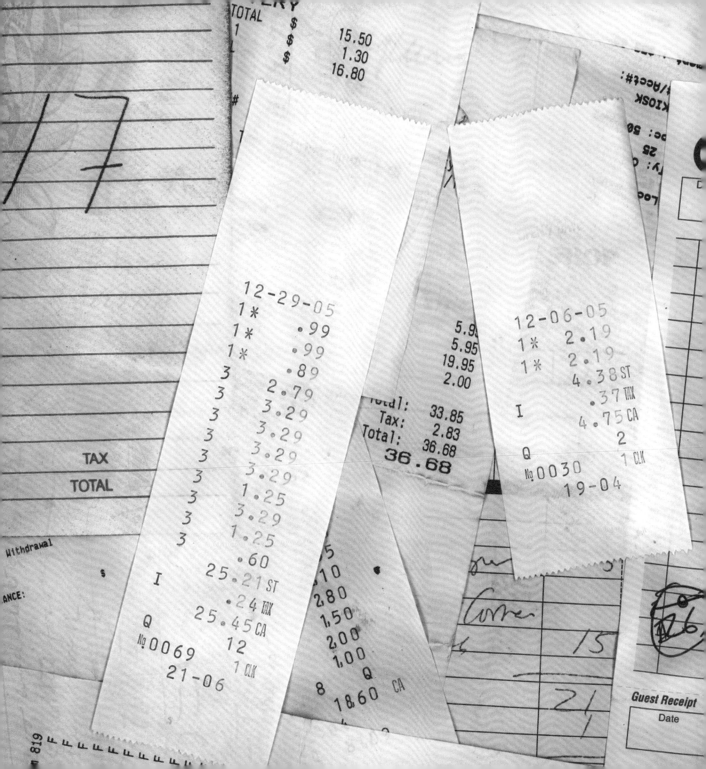

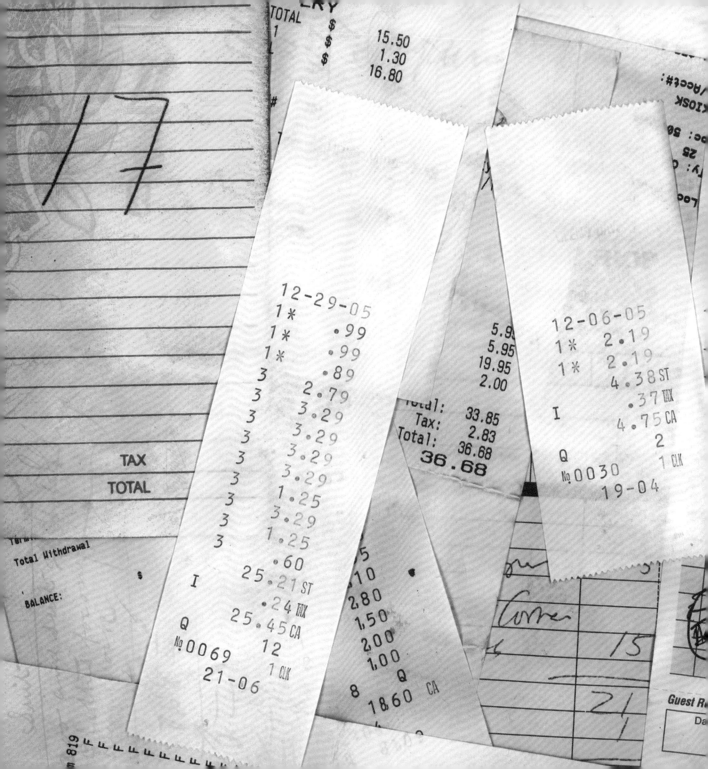

LEADER'S GUIDE

So you're the leader . . .

Is that intimidating? Perhaps exciting? No doubt you have some mental pictures of what it will look like, what you will say, and how it will go. Before you get too far into the planning process, there are some things you should know about leading a small group discussion. We've compiled some tried and true techniques to help you.

BASICS ABOUT LEADING

1. **Don't teach . . . facilitate** – Perhaps you've been in a Sunday school class or Bible study where the leader could answer any question and always had something interesting to say. It's easy to think you need to be like that too. Relax. You don't. Leading a small group is quite different. Instead of being the featured act at the party, think of yourself as the host or hostess behind the scenes. Your primary job is to create a comfortable environment and to keep the meeting generally on track. Your party is most successful when your guests do most of the talking.

2. **Cultivate discussion** – It's also easy to think that the meeting lives or dies by your ideas. In reality, the ideas of everyone in the group are what make a small group meeting successful. The most valuable thing you can do is to get people to share their thoughts. That's how the relationships in your group will thrive. Here's a rule: The impact of your study material will never exceed the impact of the relationships through which it was studied. The more meaningful the relationships, the more meaningful the study. In a sterile environment, even the best material is ineffective.

3. **Point to the material** – A good host or hostess gets the party going by offering delectable hors d'oeuvres and beverages. You, too, should be ready to serve up "delicacies" from the material. Sometimes you will simply read the discussion questions and invite everyone to respond. At other times, you will encourage others to share their ideas. Remember, some of the best treats are the ones your guests bring to the party. Go with the flow of the meeting, and be ready to pop out of the kitchen as needed.

4. **Depart from the material** – We have carefully designed this study for your small group. But that doesn't mean you should follow every part word for word. Knowing how and when to depart from the material is a valuable art. Nobody knows more about your people than you do. The narratives, questions, and exercises are here to provide a framework for discovery. However, every group is motivated differently. Sometimes the best way to start a small group discussion is simply to ask, "Does anyone have a personal insight or revelation you'd like to share from this week's material?" Then sit back and listen.

5. **Stay on track** – Conversation is the currency of a small group discussion. The more interchange, the healthier the "economy." However, you need to keep your objectives in mind. If your goal is to have a meaningful experience with this material, then you should make sure the discussion is contributing to that end. It's easy to get off on a tangent. Be prepared to politely refocus the group. You might need to say something like, "Excuse me, we're obviously all interested in this subject; however, I just want to make sure we cover all the material for this week."

6. **Above all, pray** – The best communicators are the ones who manage to get out of God's way enough to let him communicate through them. That's important to keep in mind. Books don't teach God's Word; neither do sermons nor group discussions. God himself speaks into the hearts of men and women, and prayer is our vital channel to communicate directly with him. Cover your efforts in prayer. You don't just want God present at your meeting . . . you want him to direct it.

We hope you find these suggestions helpful. And we hope you enjoy leading this study. You will find additional guidelines and suggestions for each session in the Leader's Guide notes that follow.

LEADER'S GUIDE
SESSION NOTES

Session 1 – Opening the Books

BOTTOM LINE

A study in finances is much more than simply developing a strategy for reducing debt or tracking purchases. The way we handle our finances has a lot to say about our relationship with God. We cannot divorce our faith from our identities as fathers or daughters or students. Similarly, we cannot compartmentalize our lives to include God in most decisions, yet leave him out of a discussion regarding our finances.

In this first session, we learn that your treasure follows your heart. For some of your group members, a study of finances might have been a long time coming. For others, it might indeed be a sudden realization that faith and finances are very much intertwined.

PRACTICAL APPLICATION

This exercise is intended to establish a baseline for our financial stability. As is the case with most things in life, you never know how to reach a particular destination until you understand where you're coming from. Since this is something the group members will be doing for the entire study, it is important to make sure that all members of the group are tracking their weekly expenses. You can ask them to either use the ledger provided in this study guide or some other tracking tool that they are already using. Understandably, some group members might be extremely private about their finances. Group members don't have to share exact numbers regarding their expenses. Instead, it's important for everyone to track expenses and, as the leader, you'll want to encourage some accountability to make sure that this application is exercised each week.

DISCUSSION STARTER

Depending on the dynamics in the group, this question could generate a lot of conversation. You can ask some follow-up questions about successful or unsuccessful components of previous financial studies that group members have experienced.

VIDEO SEGMENT

Watch the video clip for this session with your group.

NOTES FOR DISCUSSION QUESTIONS

1. Do you agree that it is impossible to be a committed follower of Jesus Christ and remain financially irresponsible? Why or why not?

This question uncovers the truth that our understanding of finances reflects a lot about our faith. Hopefully, this is a conclusion that your group members will reach intuitively. Otherwise, you can ask which other areas of life we tend to separate from our faith.

2. What are some of the things that cause people to become financially unbalanced?

Because finances can be a very private matter for some, you'll want to make sure that your group meeting is a safe environment during this study. The more your members feel comfortable to be authentic with the group regarding their finances, the more beneficial this study will be— both in achieving financial health and developing group chemistry.

3. Read Matthew 6:21. What are some examples in your life of your heart following your stuff?

4. Read Luke 16:13. How does our stuff compete with our devotion to God?

As with other curriculum, it's easy to provide black and white answers that don't challenge anyone's way of thinking or living. Of course, most people believe that money should not be their master and that giving to charitable causes is a positive financial decision. During these two questions, you might want to offer a more gray/obscure example to encourage more personal levels of discussion.

5. *When it comes to your finances, what do you think God wants for you (as opposed to what most people think he wants from you)?*

Given the public notoriety of certain camps of Christianity, it's easy to assume that all God or the church wants is more of our money. And if that's the assumption that most group members carry throughout this study, then these next six weeks will be very discouraging. That's why this question is intended to get your group to look at finances beyond just giving or tithing to the church. The objective is to look at the larger picture. You can ask why they think a person's financial freedom would be so important to God.

6. *How easy is it for you to trust God with your finances? What would you do differently if you were confident that God wanted the best for you in that area?*

Regardless of what people say, trusting an invisible God with our very tangible finances is a difficult thing to do. This question is intended to help group members look at the positive aspects of trusting God with their finances. As a follow-up question, you can ask group members about certain areas of their finances where they already feel God is asking them to trust him.

7. *What would you like to see happen in your finances as a result of this study?*

As with many introductory chapters, this question allows your group the opportunity to discuss what they want to get out of this study. Allow the responses from this question to help you tailor the discussion times for the weeks to come.

Flip a Coin

While all the principles taught through this study surface throughout the pages of the Bible, the contemporary applications of these principles can vary widely depending on the particular context. As a result, these "Flip a Coin" segments are designed to introduce a level of real-life tension.

Are there right or wrong answers? As a group leader, you might feel the need to alleviate the tension with a definitive answer, a resolution. Keep in mind that as with most things in life, real-life financial decisions rarely have a black or white answer. Your job is to facilitate the conversation for your group, and continue to model a posture of seeking wisdom as you pursue financial balance.

A question about your heart...

The tension for Session 1 explores the idea of serving money while seemingly living a balanced financial life. Is it possible to have sound financial principles, a generous lifestyle...and still serve Money as a master?

Session 2 – Reading the Fine Print

Bottom Line

Our perspectives on our finances will drastically change when we start seeing God as the giver of all things. We will begin to understand that God owns everything; and we have been entrusted as stewards of his gifts, monies, and assets. The passage from 1 Chronicles 29 clearly illustrates the idea that we are stewards and caretakers. In this session, the goal is to help your group members view their finances from a higher perspective, one that asks the question, "How do I honor God with everything I have?"

Practical Application

This two-part application includes the weekly financial tracking exercise. But this week, your group members should also be filling out the Financial Overview included in this study guide (or a comparable Financial Overview tool), as well as on the accompanying DVD found in the back of the study guide. During this week's study, you'll be looking at a different perspective on ownership. Similarly, the Financial Overview tool will help your group members look at their finances from a higher-level perspective rather than a peripheral, week-to-week, or month-to-month point of view.

Discussion Starter

You can also ask the group members if they made any major/minor changes to their spending habits this past week as a result of tracking their daily spending. Take the opportunity to develop guidelines for making sure the Practical Application exercises are completed each week.

Video Segment

Watch the video clip for this session with your group.

NOTES FOR DISCUSSION QUESTIONS

1. *Up to this point, what has been your goal regarding your money? What has been the main influence on your financial decisions?*

As always, these first questions, along with the Discussion Starter, are meant to spark discussion in the group. If your group members have always had it in mind to "honor God" with their money, then be prepared to ask a follow-up question that raises a little bit of tension for your discussion time.

2. *What does it mean to "honor God" with your life on a day-to-day basis as it relates to your finances?*

Have some specific cultural applications in mind. Could honoring God be reflected in the way we choose a job? Could honoring God be reflected in our spending habits? Could honoring God be reflected in the way we understand our giving options?

3. *In 1 Chronicles 29, David seems to understand that God was the source of all of the resources available to him. What is the difference between stewardship and ownership? Why is it hard to see yourself as a steward rather than an owner?*

4. *How would it change your financial decisions to see yourself as a steward of God's gifts and resources?*

For some members in your group, this study might be the first time they've considered themselves as stewards as opposed to owners. As a result, it might raise some discussion about ownership versus stewardship. It might also raise some questions about what exactly God wants us to do with our finances: What does it mean to further his kingdom? Does that consist of giving away all our money to orphans and widows? Or is there more involved in stewardship than just deciding to which charities to donate?

5. *How have people used their money and "stuff" to make an eternal impact on your life?*

Some of your group members might not resonate with the idea of eternal value or eternal impact. For them, using the term "priceless" can be a start to measuring financial decisions beyond immediate returns. And for others, it might help to explain that financial decisions with "eternal" implications aren't simply about giving money to help people get to heaven, but also about leveraging money with a kingdom-stewardship mentality.

6. *How can you use the money and "stuff" that God has given you as tools to make an eternal impact on others?*

In this study, there is a weekly Practical Application exercise to help your group begin to see their finances from a larger, but more pragmatic perspective. The last one or two questions in each section are designed to encourage some type of action step or personal application around the key point for that week. As the group wraps up the discussion section for this week, ask group members about specific financial decisions they can make this week in order to make an impact on others (with the thought of sharing those stories the following week).

FLIP A COIN

A question about tithing…

Last week, the group looked at the tension of serving money as a master. In Session 2, the discipline of tithing is explored. Specifically, how much should I regularly give to God? Realizing that God owns everything we have, are we as stewards commanded to give according to the needs we see around us? Or does it honor God to give a consistent percentage on a regular basis?

As a leader, be sure to keep in mind that the "Flip a Coin" segments are designed to introduce a level of real-life tension. You might find that people have distinct ideas about what constitutes tithing. The goal is to continue to facilitate conversation while seeking financial wisdom.

Bottom Line

Debt isn't just about having negative entries in your ledger. It's about exchanging financial slavery for financial freedom. That's why the Bible speaks so clearly about staying out of debt. Debt might not be an issue for some members in your group. However, if the makeup of your group reflects the current cultural landscape, then there will definitely be some members that are struggling to maintain their financial freedom. But no matter how indebted they might feel, there is hope. They are not alone. Both God and, hopefully, this small group can provide direction toward financial freedom and accountability.

Practical Application

The Debt Repayment Plan found in the Appendix and on the DVD is a very simple tool to use. Members of your group might suggest other tools or software that they have been using to gauge their debt repayment plans. There is no single tool that is perfect for everyone. However, the goal of this application is to bring the reality of debt to the surface. It does no good to ignore debt and hope it eventually goes away. By following the steps in this application, your group members are being intentional about understanding and eradicating debt in their lives.

Discussion Starter

This question should raise plenty of discussion. Although the strategies listed in the Practical Application should be very helpful, group members might offer different suggestions regarding the best methods for attacking debt. Instead of letting this discussion be a platform for whose financial house is in the best order and who has the best strategy, you'll want to encourage a safe, nonthreatening, noncompetitive environment that ensures that group members understand they are not alone as they get out (or stay out) of debt.

Video Segment

Watch the video clip for this session with your group.

Notes for Discussion Questions

1. Describe your family of origin's approach to finances. Were things tight? How did they use debt? Was it a source of tension for your family?

2. What has been your experience with debt?

Hopefully, by this point, your group members feel enough freedom to share from their own experiences. Be prepared to open with your own experience with debt.

3. In what ways does debt limit freedom? Can you give any personal examples?

Numerous passages from the Bible compare debt to enslavement. Again, the Bible reveals truth that is supported by our experiences. As a follow-up question, you can ask, "What are some opportunities that you might not have been able to take advantage of because you were living in debt?"

4. What makes it so difficult to get out of debt?

For most people, personal finances are private matters. And debt is an associated topic that is rarely discussed outside of the home. As a result, this study might be the first time that your group members share about their financial principles. As the group leader, you might want to communicate to the group again that this is a safe environment to share as much or as little as they are comfortable with. This question provides the space for members to safely discuss how they have seen "others" or themselves get into debt.

5. What are the benefits of living debt-free?

Again, you'll want this discussion time to encourage your group members to take positive steps forward. Having heard the couple's story from the video, as well as from the experiences shared in the group, you might want to ask the group about definitive next steps that they will take this week in order to get out (or stay out) of debt.

6. Is going into debt always unwise? When is it wise?

Some financial experts suggest there are various forms of healthy debt. Other experts suggest that all debt is unhealthy. You might find differences of opinion in your discussion. Group members might start sharing specific financial strategies and principles. However, unless it's a unique situation, don't allow this time to be an isolated, "fix-it" consultation for a specific group member.

FLIP A COIN

A question about debt...

In the last session, we looked at tithing and the real-life tension that this discipline can evoke. In this session, we looked at the issue of debt. The Bible seems clear on its position regarding debt. However, the world presents an alternate view.

Are there life circumstances that necessitate going into debt?

What are some examples of "wise" or "foolish" debt?

What safeguards have you created to ensure that the debt you are incurring is indeed "wise" debt?

These are just a few of the questions that bring this tension to bear.

As a leader, your tendency might be to respond to this tension immediately. Be sure to allow the conversation to develop.

Session 4 – Creating a New Line Item

Bottom Line

Compared to the rest of the world's inhabitants, you are much richer than you think. God has blessed you with food, clothes, and a home. Sure, you might not be able to afford your dream car, but chances are, you won't starve tonight. That's more than a majority around the globe can say. But the key point in this session is not to make you feel uncomfortable with the abundance that you've been given. Instead, the key point is to realize that we've been given much so we can give much.

Practical Application

Continue to encourage your group members to track their weekly spending. As a group, you can discuss any new methods of tracking or any special realizations that the members are noticing in their spending patterns. You'll want to discuss the Giving Plan that is provided in the Appendix and the DVD. For some members of your group, a regular, dedicated habit of giving might be a foreign idea. Having a discussion around the reasons to give can be much healthier than simply suggesting that there is a biblical mandate to give. There should be plenty of discussion regarding the Giving Plan, which should set you up for the following discussion questions.

Discussion Starter

Most people enjoy the feeling they get from helping others. Discuss why people don't give more often as you talk about the helpfulness of the Giving Plan.

Video Segment

Watch the video clip for this session with your group.

1. *Do you consider yourself to be rich? Why or why not?*

Discuss different definitions of "rich." Given the median income level of those living in the United States, most people living outside the U.S. would consider us rich by any standard. The hope is that your group members will realize that they have been blessed with a certain level of abundance.

2. *Why is it so difficult to recognize greed in the mirror? What are some of the signs?*

When the only thing you're focusing on is yourself, you have no connection to anyone else's reality. For example, if you live with five toasters in a neighborhood where everyone has five toasters, then it never occurs to you that having five toasters might be a bit much. Discuss some steps the group can take to help recognize greed in their lives.

3. *What prevents us from sharing what we have with others?*

One reason people might not share with others is the fear of not having enough. Yet, God promises to provide for our needs. You can discuss times when you stepped forward in generosity to find out that God took care of you. Additionally, you can discuss the difference between reluctance to share and being selective about whom you're going to share with.

4. *When have you been able to meet someone else's needs? How did that feel?*

Most people enjoy the satisfaction of helping others. When we are able to bless others, our sacrificial acts usually result in our own sense of being blessed. For example, many people that go on short-term mission trips respond by saying that they felt more blessed than those they were able to help.

5. *Why is it important to be a consistent and percentage giver?*

6. *What steps can you take to consistently practice generosity with your finances?*

These last two questions provide an action step for this week's session. You might want to give your group members a few minutes to think about some ways they can be rich toward God this week. Remember, this study guide is meant to not only promote discussion around our finances, but also to encourage healthy life change around our finances. Being a consistent giver builds within us a discipline of being generous; it helps us to have an open-handed attitude about our stuff. Be prepared to discuss the importance of giving to the local church, especially with group members that might have had negative experiences with money-hungry Christian organizations.

Flip a Coin

A question about giving…

As you continue to facilitate conversation around real-life issues of financial balance, you will eventually talk about the relationship of giving and debt.

The discussion in this session is an opportunity to explore the reality of giving while struggling with debt. Should we give first or pay off our debts first? Are we being irresponsible if we don't pay off our debts first? These are just a couple of the tensions that your group will want to wrestle with.

Session 5 – Managing Your Spending

Bottom Line

Discontentment is a reality of life. Finding a way to acknowledge and channel our discontentment in healthy ways is a step in addressing our desire for more material stuff. If our goal is to become richer, then no amount of money or riches will make us content. Instead, the Bible tells us to make a conscious decision to pursue something else. The Bible tells us to pursue generosity—leveraging our wealth for other people—in order to find genuine contentment.

Practical Application

This exercise will provide an accurate picture of your group's spending patterns during the past month. Instead of guessing how much they spend on food or entertainment, now they have a detailed snapshot of how they're spending their money. Ask, "Is this where you wanted your money to go?"

Discussion Starter

These discussion starters are meant to provide some accountability for the group in completing each week's Practical Application. Some group members might feel comfortable enough to share the details of their entire spending patterns with the rest of the group. However, it might be safer to ask your group members to share about one or two areas that they found surprisingly high or low in their actual spending, as well as to ask about how their spending reflects their priorities.

Video Segment

Watch the video clip for this session with your group.

Notes for Discussion Questions

1. *"Discontentment is robbing our generation." Do you agree with this statement? If so, why?*

2. *Has an increase in your income satisfied your appetite? How does your income level affect your level of contentment?*

We tend to think that if we ever win the lottery or hit a jackpot, we will be set for life. Yet, when we do receive additional money, we usually get to a point where we feel like we need more. Discuss times when this might or might not have been the case.

3. *What is the danger that comes with "being rich"? How have you seen this in your life and the lives of others?*

This question illustrates why becoming materially rich might not lead to contentment. We've all heard stories about lottery winners wishing they had never won it because of the additional problems that ensued. Discuss your own experiences of problems or dangers from living in abundance.

4. *Where do you need to draw the line and be content with what you have?*

For many people in this world, the line might be having just enough to get through the day. Others might be content with having enough to get through the week, month, or six months (as some financial experts suggest). Instead of focusing on a quantitative benchmark, this question aims to identify the need to be content instead of always wanting more.

5. *What are the benefits of being rich in good deeds and generous to others?*

Regardless of a person's relationship or lack of a relationship with God, most people feel some sense of satisfaction in helping others. Since your group might consist of both believers and nonbelievers, feel free to discuss how faith in God results in different answers to this question.

6. *What could you do this week to fight discontentment by becoming more aware of what someone else doesn't have?*

Again, this last question aims to encourage some type of action step for the following week. Discuss ways that group members can express richness toward God and others in order to satisfy their discontentment. Tell your group members to be prepared to share from their experiences at the next session.

FLIP A COIN

A question about spending...

What does it mean to honor God with your financial lifestyle? Are Christians called to live within their means or to live more simply? Does living more simply equate to having less stuff or more inexpensive stuff? These are the conversations that your group will have in this session.

As you guide your group through the tension of our spending habits and lifestyles, you will find members at both extremes. Conversation is the key component to remember.

Session 6 – Developing a Plan

BOTTOM LINE

The key point in this session is to help you and your group members make wise decisions by implementing a habit of give, save, live. We can study and discuss financial strategies and stories of financial successes and failures, but until we take specific steps, we'll never realize the freedom in surrendering our finances to God.

PRACTICAL APPLICATION

Have group members share some specifics about the budgets they have developed or benchmarks they hope to reach so that the group can support them in reaching their financial goals. As expressed in the video clip, ask why it is that creditors and financial institutions that only see us as account numbers have full access to our financial histories, and we choose to keep those who actually care about us the most (e.g., our community group) in the dark about our financial habits.

DISCUSSION STARTER

Along with discussing the Practical Application, use this time to share some future goals regarding their financial priorities. Do some group members want to alleviate X amount of debt in X months? Do some group members hope to make some changes to reduce their eating-out budgets? The point of this exercise is to create an environment where your community group can be a place of financial accountability.

VIDEO SEGMENT

Watch the video clip for this session with your group.

NOTES FOR DISCUSSION QUESTIONS

1. Why does it make sense to live off a percentage of your income?

Most people aren't aware of how much of their income they are saving/spending. Yet, everyone lives off a percentage. Some live off 80 percent. Some live off 105 percent. Ask: "Why not make it your own choice and be intentional about living off a predetermined amount?" Discuss how it could be easy to end up living off more than they're actually making.

2. What challenges might prevent you from setting apart a portion of your income and practicing "give, save, live"?

The idea of "give, save, live" might be foreign for some members in your group. As people comment on different challenges, you can also ask those who have already adopted this mentality to share what it has been like to consider "giving" as their first priority.

3. Does it matter what percentages you choose to give, save, and live on? Have you heard any helpful suggestions from financial experts? Does the Bible offer any suggestions?

In response to this question, look at what the Bible might have suggested in the Old Testament and then what the New Testament advises regarding giving generously.

4. What are some good benchmark percentages for you to consider?

Allocating 10 percent of your income to giving, 10 percent of your income to saving, and 80 percent of your income to spending is a good first step. For some people in your group, that might not be possible and only a goal for them to pursue. The point is to choose a percentage and start there.

5. Prior to this study, how intentional were you (if at all) about allocating a certain percentage of your income to giving, saving, and living?

In addition to questions 4 and 5, if you are in a group with other married couples with children, discuss ways you can help your children develop a similar "give, save, live" habit.

6. Going forward, what is your plan for staying out of debt?

You might want to review some of the steps from Session 3 in regards to tackling debt. Pray. Stop incurring new debt. Set up an emergency fund. You can ask your group members how intentional they have been toward implementing these steps the past several weeks.

7. *How will you manage the money and possessions that God has given you differently because of this study?*

Use this question to discuss any final thoughts about this study. Ask if anyone has been challenged to live differently or to rearrange his or her financial habits. Ask if seeing their roles as stewards instead of owners challenges their financial principles. Ask what steps they can take to continue to place God at the center of their finances.

Even though this study has ended, our understanding of God and finances will continue to affect our financial decisions and practices. Discuss some ways your group can stay connected in order to maintain accountability in the financial area of their lives.

FLIP A COIN

A question about saving…

Last session, we looked at the real-life tension of how our spending might or might not reflect our hearts. This time, we look at the other side of spending—saving.

Is there a difference between saving for the future and hoarding a stockpile of wealth? Unhealthy spending habits might be easy to detect. But can there be an unhealthy aspect to saving? Once again, you might find that your group members have wildly contrasting perspectives. The goal is not to alleviate the tension, but to help your group members achieve balance, particularly in the areas of saving and spending.

Notes

{Your Name Here}
STEWARD OF GOD'S RESOURCES